LET'S ALL GO! THE NATIONAL PARKS

63 PARKS!

ILLUSTRATED BY JEN RACINE

ADVENTURE COLORING BOOK

THIS BOOK BELONGS TO

ABOUT THIS BOOK

THIS BOOK IS INTENDED TO BE AN INTRODUCTION TO ALL OF THE NATIONAL PARKS OF THE USA.

EACH PAGE FEATURES:

1 MAP OUTLINE OF EACH PARK
*NOTE: ROADS ARE INDICATED BUT MAY NOT BE ENTIRELY ACCURATE. IF THERE ARE NO ROADS ON THE MAP THIS PARK IS ONLY ACCESSIBLE BY AIRPLANE OR BOAT (DRAWING).

2 TWO MAMMALS
*ONE MIGHT BE A BIRD

THIS MEANS WATER

3 TWO PLANTS
*SOMETIMES THREE

4 ONE ICONIC SIGHT AT THE PARK *THERE ARE MANY BEAUTIFUL THINGS TO SEE AT EACH PARK - THIS IS ONE THAT MIGHT BE A "MUST-SEE". A FEW PAGES ARE WHAT YOU WILL SEE AT THE PARK (UNLABELED).

USE THE INTERNET TO LOOK UP THE PLANTS AND ANIMALS IN THIS BOOK! YOU CAN GET IDEAS FOR COLORS AND LEARN MORE ABOUT EACH.

FYI

ALL 63 PARKS ARE IN THIS BOOK. HOWEVER, TWO PAGES HAVE TWO PARKS PER PAGE BECAUSE THEY ARE VERY CLOSE TOGETHER — SEQUOIA & KINGS CANYON AND EVERGLADES & BISCAYNE.

AND

INFORMATION FOR NATIONAL PARKS WAS FOUND USING VARIOUS INTERNET SOURCES INCLUDING WIKIPEDIA AND TRAVEL SITES. ALL INFORMATION WAS ASSUMED ACCURATE AND CURRENT AT TIME OF PUBLICATION.

COLORING TIPS!

PUT A PIECE OF PAPER BEHIND THE PAGE YOU ARE COLORING IF YOU ARE USING MARKERS— THIS HELPS PREVENT BLEED-THROUGH AND CREASING ON THE NEXT PAGE. COLORED PENCILS, CRAYON OR LIGHT MARKERS ARE MOST SUITABLE FOR THIS PAPER.

FIND ME

instagram: @jenracinecoloring

facebook.com/jenracinecoloring

www.jenracine.com

ALSO ON ETSY FOR COLORING PAGES@
www.etsy.com/shop/JenRacineColoring

Copyright © 2023 by Eclectic Esquire Media LLC
ISBN: 978-1-958048-31-3

RIVER OTTER

RHODORA

PEREGRINE FALCON

ACADIA

NATIONAL

PARK

MAINE

PINK LADY SLIPPER

ATLANTIC PUFFIN

BASS HARBOR LIGHTHOUSE

WESTERN COLLARED LIZARD

NATIONAL PARK
ARCHES
UTAH

WINDOWS SECTION

PRICKLY PEAR CACTUS

YUCCA PLANT

KANGAROO RAT

DELICATE ARCH

SPINY PHLOX

SOUTH DAKOTA

PRAIRIE RATTLESNAKE

PINNACLES OVERLOOK

WESTERN WHEATGRASS

BISON

PURPLE CONEFLOWER

BADLANDS

NATIONAL PARK

SANTA ELENA CANYON TRAIL

MESQUITE

BIG BEND BLUEBONNET

NATIONAL PARK

TEXAS

BIG BEND

BLACKFOOT DAISY

BLACK TAILED JACKRABBIT

BLACK BEAR

CANYON WREN

UTAH

MESA ARCH

EVENING PRIMROSE

DESERT BIGHORN SHEEP

SMOOTH HORSETAIL

CANYONLANDS
NATIONAL PARK

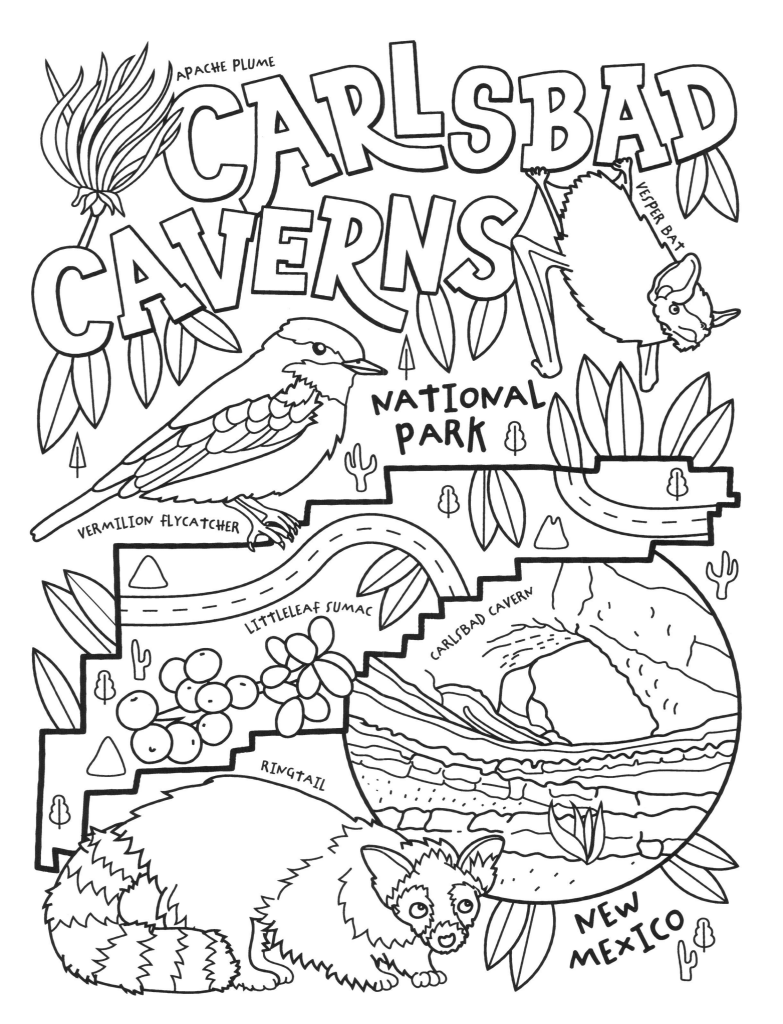

CARLSBAD CAVERNS

APACHE PLUME

VESPER BAT

NATIONAL PARK

VERMILION FLYCATCHER

LITTLELEAF SUMAC

CARLSBAD CAVERN

RINGTAIL

NEW MEXICO

OHIO

CARDINAL

CUYAHOGA VALLEY
NATIONAL PARK

YELLOW

TROUT LILY

NEW ENGLAND ASTER

COYOTE

BRANDYWINE FALLS

AMERICAN MINK

MOUNTAIN HEATHER

ALASKA

MOUNTAIN AVENS

MOUNT DENALI

GRIZZLY BEAR

KAHILTNA GLACIER

FORGET-ME-NOT

SNOWSHOE HARE

DENALI
NATIONAL PARK

DRY TORTUGAS NATIONAL PARK

BROWN NODDIE

LOGGERHEAD TURTLE

ANGELFISH

FORT JEFFERSON

GARDEN KEY

ELKHORN CORAL

BUSH KEY

NURSE SHARK

FLORIDA

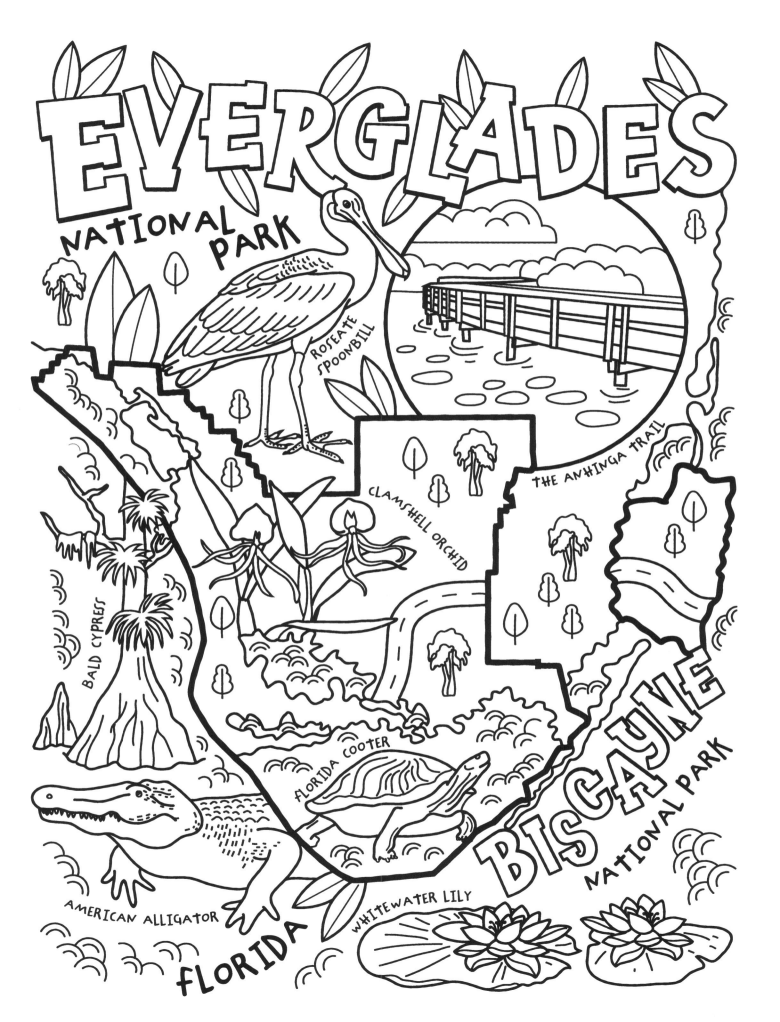

EVERGLADES

NATIONAL PARK

ROSEATE SPOONBILL

THE ANHINGA TRAIL

CLAMSHELL ORCHID

BALD CYPRESS

AMERICAN ALLIGATOR

FLORIDA COOTER

FLORIDA

WHITEWATER LILY

BISCAYNE

NATIONAL PARK

ALASKA

MARGERIE GLACIER

CHOCOLATE LILY

BALD EAGLE

DEVIL'S CLUB

INDIAN PAINTBRUSH

GLACIER BAY

NATIONAL PARK

BLACK BEAR

MOUNT FAIRWEATHER

DUSTY STAR MOUNTAIN

BEAR GRASS

MONTANA

NATIONAL PARK

PURPLE ASTER

MOUNTAIN GOAT

WOLVERINE

GLACIER

GRAND TETON
NATIONAL PARK

GRAND TETON

RED FOX

MOOSE

LARKSPUR

SKYROCKET GILIA

YELLOW MONKEY FLOWER

WYOMING

MIDDLE TETON

BOBCAT

LEHMAN CAVES

SAGEBRUSH

GOLDEN EAGLE

INDIAN PAINTBRUSH

NEVADA

GREAT BASIN

NATIONAL PARK

COLORADO

ORD'S KANGAROO RAT

SAND VERBENA

STAR DUNE

AMERICAN BADGER

PRAIRIE SUNFLOWER

GREAT SAND DUNES

NATIONAL PARK

TENNESSEE

WHITE-TAILED DEER

RAINBOW FALLS

FLAME AZALEA

WILD BLUE PHLOX

WOODCHUCK

SHOWY ORCHIS

CADES COVE

GREAT SMOKY MOUNTAINS NATIONAL PARK

TEXAS

BANANA YUCCA

GUADALUPE PEAK

ROCK SQUIRREL

GUADALUPE MOUNTAINS

MULE DEER

SANTA FE PHLOX

NATIONAL PARK

HAWAI'I

HAWAIIAN HONEYCREEPER

HALEAKALĀ CRATER

HALEAKALĀ SILVERSWORDS

SILVER GERANIUM

GREEN SEA TURTLE

HALEAKALĀ

NATIONAL PARK

ŌHI'A TREE

HAWAIIAN GOOSE (NENE)

HAWAI'I VOLCANOES

NATIONAL PARK

MAUNA LOA VOLCANO

KI PLANT

PAHOEHOE LAVA

KILAUEA VOLCANO

HAWAI'I

HAWAIIAN GREEN SEA TURTLE

KOA TREE

DUNES SUCCESSION TRAIL

RED BEE BALM

INDIANA

NATIONAL PARK

INDIANA DUNES

SANDHILL CRANE

EASTERN COTTONTAIL

BUTTERFLY WEED

MICHIGAN

SKUNK CABBAGE

RED SQUIRREL

ISLE ROYALE

NATIONAL PARK

CALYPSO ORCHID

GRAY WOLF

KENAI FJORDS

HARDING ICEFIELD

NOOTKA LUPINE

NATIONAL PARK

MOUNTAIN CRANBERRY

ORCA

ALASKA

HARBOR SEAL

ALASKA

RED FOX

ALASKA COTTON GRASS

LAKE CLARK

BOG STAR

ALPINE BLUEBERRY

BLACK BEAR

LAKE CLARK

NATIONAL PARK & NATIONAL PRESERVE

LASSEN VOLCANIC

NATIONAL PARK

STELLER'S JAY

LASSEN PAINTBRUSH

BUMPASS HELL BASIN

MULES EAR

SIERRA NEVADA RED FOX

CALIFORNIA

GEYSERS PANICUM GRASS

COTTONTAIL RABBIT

COLORADO

YUCCA

OREGON GRAPE

GREAT HORNED OWL

EVENING PRIMROSE

CLIFF PALACE

ROCK GOLDENROD

MESA VERDE

NATIONAL PARK

WASHINGTON

OSPREY

DIABLO LAKE OVERLOOK

SWORD FERN

HOARY MARMOT

RED COLUMBINE

NORTH CASCADES

NATIONAL PARK

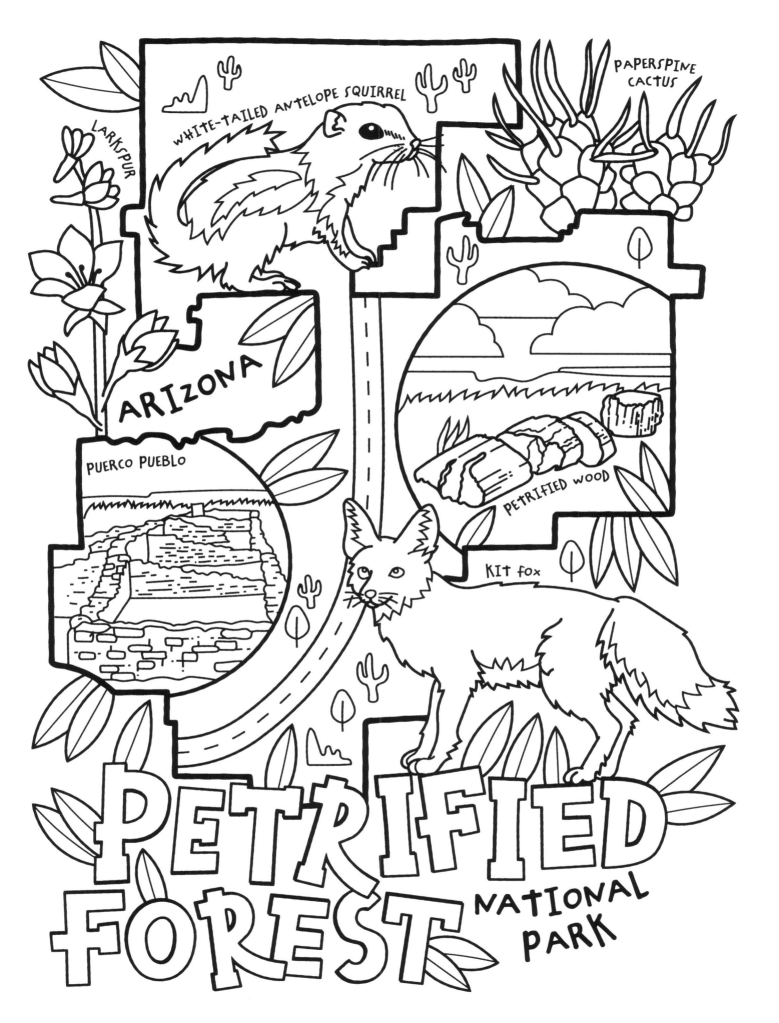

PAPERSPINE CACTUS

WHITE-TAILED ANTELOPE SQUIRREL

LARKSPUR

ARIZONA

PUERCO PUEBLO

PETRIFIED WOOD

KIT FOX

PETRIFIED FOREST NATIONAL PARK

HEPATICA

SHENANDOAH NATIONAL PARK

SPOTTED SKUNK

BLOODROOT

STONY MAN CLIFFS

BLACK BEAR

VIRGINIA

THEODORE ROOSEVELT

NATIONAL PARK

RABBITBRUSH

NORTH DAKOTA

PASQUE FLOWER

PRAIRIE DOG

MALTESE CROSS CABIN

BLACK-CAPPED CHICKADEE

BISON

BURROWING OWL

KIT FOX

CAVE CHOLLA

WHITE SAND DUNES

OCOTILLO

NATIONAL PARK

WHITE SANDS

NEW MEXICO

APACHE POCKET MOUSE

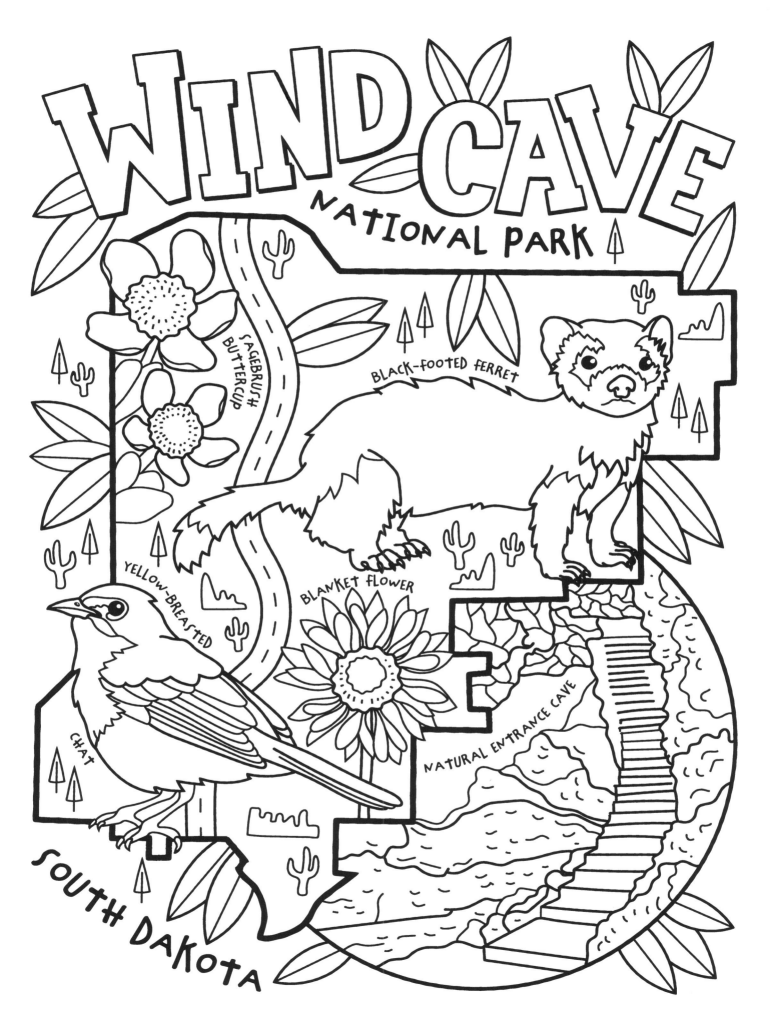

Made in the USA
Las Vegas, NV
14 July 2023

74739499R00070